A man had a cat on
his tug.

Lil and Don ran to
get on the tug.

The sun was up, but
it was not hot.

Don had a rod and
Lil had a rod.

The man had a big
net.

Don got a tug on
his rod.
The cat sat up.

Don had to tug, but
it was a lot of fun.

Lil had a rod and the man had a net.

Lil got a big tug on
the rod.

Lil had to tug on it.
It was a big job to
get a cod.

Lil got wet, but
Lil got the cod.

The man got the
cod from Lil.
The cod hit the cat.
The cat ran.

The man set the
cod in a big tub.
The cat ran up to
the tub.

Lil and Don sat and
had a can of pop.

Lil and Don ran
to get the cod.
But the cod was
not in the tub.

The cat sat in the tub,
and the cat was fat.